COUNTRY FAMILY

written by
Molly Bridger

illustrated by
Anna Rich

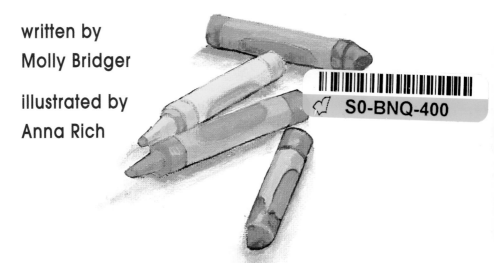

CITY FAMILY

HARCOURT BRACE & COMPANY

Orlando   Atlanta   Austin   Boston   San Francisco   Chicago   Dallas   New York
Toronto   London

My teacher asked me to draw
a picture of my family. I need a
very big sheet of paper.

I have two families. One family lives in the country. The other family lives in the city.

In my country family,
I have my mom, my
stepdad, two brothers,
and two sisters.

I love my big country family. We live on a farm with two dogs, four cows, three horses, and six cats.

In my city family, I
have my dad.

I love my small city family. We live in an apartment building on the third floor. I have six goldfish.

When I am in the country,
I eat tomatoes from the garden
and drink milk from the cows.

8

When I am in the city, Dad and
I cook a terrific meal together.

When I am with my country
family and I want an adventure,
I ride bicycles with my brother
and my sister.

When I am with my city family
and I want an adventure, I call up
my friend and we all go skating.

When I am with my country
family in the summer, we swim
in the river near our farm.

I am never lonely with my country family. There is always something to do.

When I am with my city family during the summer, we cool off at the movies.

I am never lonely with my city
family. There is always something
to do.

Here is a picture of my whole family. I have lots of people who care about me. I am so lucky to have two families!